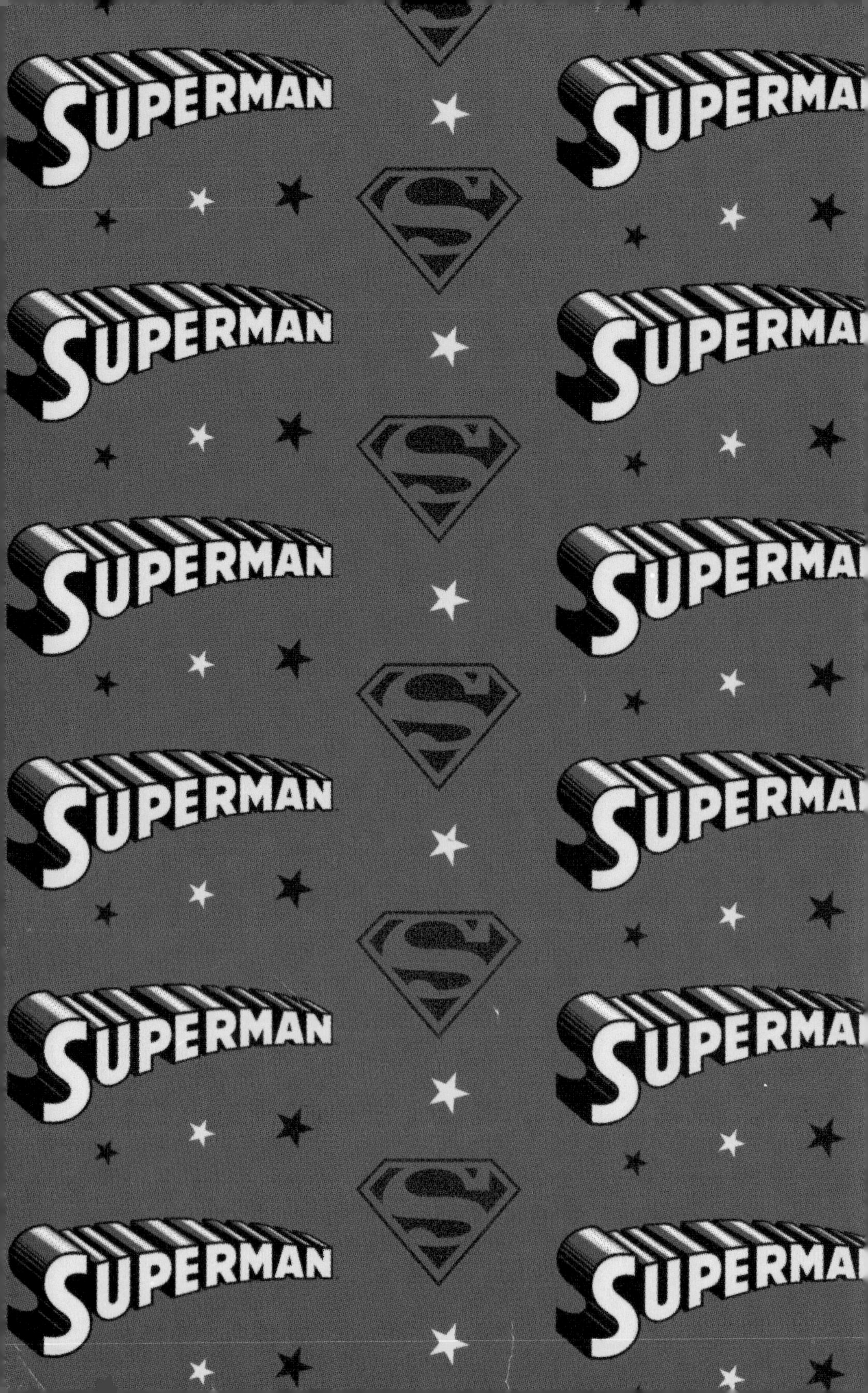
SUPERMAN

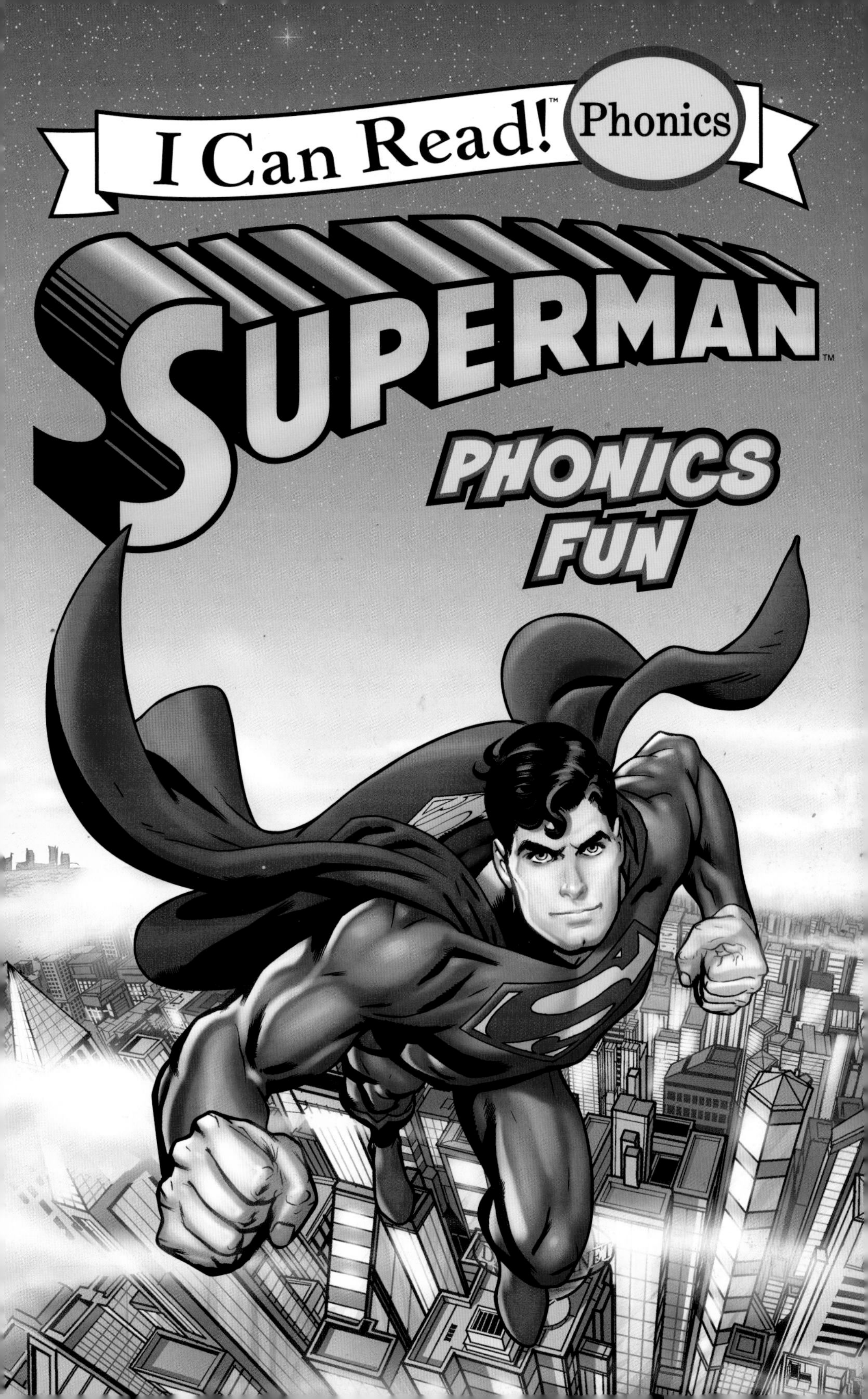
I Can Read!™ Phonics
SUPERMAN™
PHONICS FUN

HARP32233

SUPERMAN created by Jerry Siegel and Joe Shuster
By special arrangement with the Jerry Siegel family

First Edition

13 14 15 16 17 SCP 10 9 8 7 6 5 4 3 2 1

Table of Contents

Letter to Parents

Dear Parents,

Your child is about to start an exciting adventure. He or she is going to learn to read. By choosing your child's favorite characters, you have already accomplished something very important—motivation!

Superman Phonics Fun includes twelve storybooks, planned by a phonics expert. The books are intended for children to read at home with a parent or caregiver and, eventually, by themselves.

- *Superman Phonics Fun* introduces long and short vowel sounds. One of the key components in becoming a fluent reader is practice, so this set features one book for each sound, plus one introductory story and one book for review. Learning to read long and short vowels is rewarding because they are found everywhere!
- Fun Superman words have been included to make the stories rich and enjoyable.
- The stories also include sight words. These are words frequently found in books that can be hard to sound out. They just need to be learned by sight!
- Picture clues support the text in each story and help children learn new words.

As children master the sounds and words, they will gain experience and confidence in their ability to understand sounds, sound out words, and READ! Here are some suggestions for using *Superman Phonics Fun* to help your child on the road to reading:

1. Read the books aloud to your child. The first time you read a story, read it all the way through. Then invite your child to follow along by pointing out words as you read them. Encourage him or her to try to sound out new words that use familiar sounds, or that are pictured in the illustrations.

2. Discuss each sound found on the first page with your child. Help your child sound out the new words in the story. Demonstrate the vowel sounds—for example, by telling your child that the short **o** vowel sound is found in the word **hot**.

3. Look at the pictures with your child. Encourage him or her to tell the story through the pictures. Point out objects in the pictures and ask your child to name them.

We hope that you and your child enjoy *Superman Phonics Fun*, and that it is the start of many happy reading adventures.

The HarperCollins Editors

In this story you will learn new sight words.
Can you find these words?

a	are	crystal
Earth	else	has
here	his	icy
in	is	it
my	now	of
piece	planet	statues
the	there	those
what		

Superman has a secret home.

It is his Fortress of Solitude.

The fortress is in the icy Arctic.

Superman brings Lois there.

"What are those statues?"

Lois asks.

"Those are my parents,"

says Superman.

"Here, take a look."

Superman gives Lois a crystal.
"This crystal shows life on my
home planet," he says.

"What else do you keep here?"
asks Lois.

"Kryptonite," says Superman.
"It is a piece of my home planet
that can hurt me."

"I miss my planet," says Superman.

"But Earth is my home now!"

In this story you will learn about the **long a** vowel sound. Can you find these words and sound them out?

amazing	away	baby
became	came	day
late	name	named
place	raised	safe
same	save	space

Here are some sight words:

any	Earth	him	in
it	outer	planet	they
was	when		

Here are some fun Superman words:

Clark Kent   **Kal-El**   **Krypton**

When Superman was a baby,

his name was Kal-El.

He was born in outer space.

Kal-El's home was called Krypton.

It was not a safe place.

Kal-El's parents had to save him before it was too late.

They sent him away.

Kal-El came to planet Earth.

He was raised by a nice family.

They named him Clark Kent.

One day, Clark realized he

was not the same as other people.

He had amazing powers!

Clark Kent was not just any guy.

He became Superman!

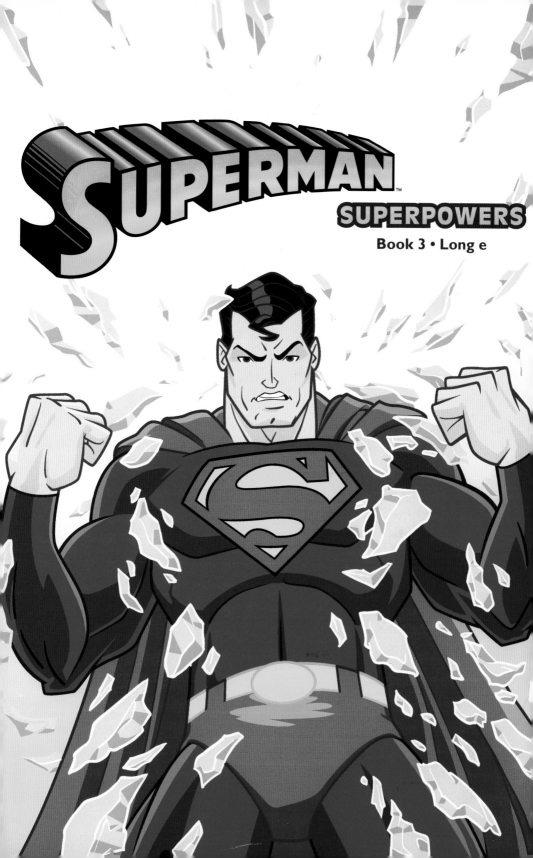

In this story you will learn about the **long e** vowel sound. Can you find these words and sound them out?

beams	beat	free
freeze	he	heat
hero	keep	secrets
see	speed	streak
weak		

Here are some sight words:

anything	anywhere	breath
eyes	icy	

Here are some fun Superman words:

kryptonite	powers	villain

Superman is a hero.

His powers make him hard
to beat.

Superman can streak across

the sky.

He can get anywhere

with super-speed.

His eyes can shoot heat beams and he can see through almost anything.

Superman's icy breath

can make things freeze.

Only one thing can make

Superman weak.

Kryptonite!

It is one of his secrets.

Superman uses his powers
to keep his city villain-free!

SUPERMAN™

METROPOLIS

Book 4 • Long i

In this story you will learn about the **long i** vowel sound. Can you find these words and sound them out?

brightly	**crime**	**finds**
guy	**hide**	**life**
likes	**mind**	**nice**
shines	**shy**	**smile**
writer	**writes**	

Here are some sight words:

about	**danger**	**friends**	**photos**
the	**there**	**wherever**	

Here are some fun Superman words:

city	***Daily Planet***	**Metropolis**

Clark Kent lives in Metropolis.

He writes about the city's crime.

Clark likes his job at the

Daily Planet.

His friends there are nice.

Jimmy Olsen takes photos.
"Smile," he says when his flash
shines brightly.

Lois Lane is a writer, too.

She doesn't hide from danger.

It finds her wherever she is!

Lois and Jimmy think
that Clark is a shy guy.
But Clark doesn't mind.

Clark has a secret life.

He is Superman!

SUPERMAN

METALLO
Book 5 • Long o

In this story you will learn about the **long o** vowel sound. Can you find these words and sound them out?

blow	bold	crows
go	glows	grows
hole	moans	no
opens	over	overhead
robot	shadow	show
stone	throws	

Here are some sight words:

again   knocks   machine   out

Here are some fun Superman words:

hook	kryptonite
Lex Luthor	Metallo

Metallo is Lex Luthor's robot.

"You must get Superman!"

Luthor crows at his machine.

Metallo opens up his chest.

The hole inside glows green.

He has a kryptonite stone inside!

Superman grows weak.

"Oh no," he moans.

How will he stop Metallo now?

Suddenly, a shadow

crosses overhead.

It's Batman!

"The show is over," he says.

Batman throws a hook at Metallo.

The stone falls out.

Superman feels bold again!

He knocks out Metallo

with one blow.

"Time to go!" says Superman.

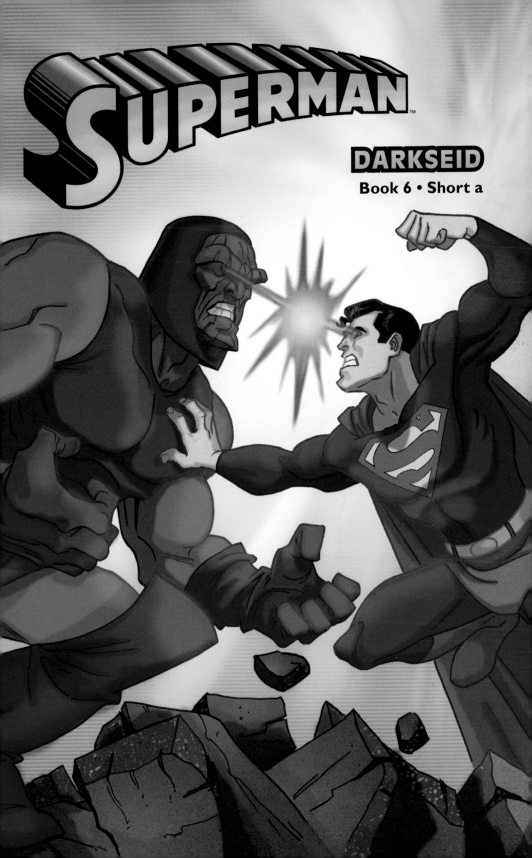

In this story you will learn about the **short a** vowel sound. Can you find these words and sound them out?

act	attacking	bad
blasts	can't	catches
chance	commands	fast
flash	lasso	man
master	plan	stand

Here are some sight words:

against   ruin   surprise   truth

Here are some fun Superman words:

| Darkseid | Metropolis |
| pals | Wonder Woman |

Darkseid is attacking Metropolis.

"Help me ruin this city!"

he orders Superman.

"Not a chance," says the Man

of Steel.

But Darkseid has a plan.

He blasts Superman with

mind-control rays.

"I am your master now!" he yells.

"Destroy Metropolis!"

Darkseid commands.

Superman can't stand up to him.

Superman's pals are here to help.

They have to act fast.

Batman catches Superman

by surprise.

In a flash, Wonder Woman throws her Lasso of Truth. Superman is freed from Darkseid's bad spell!

It's three heroes

against one bad guy.

Darkseid doesn't stand a chance!

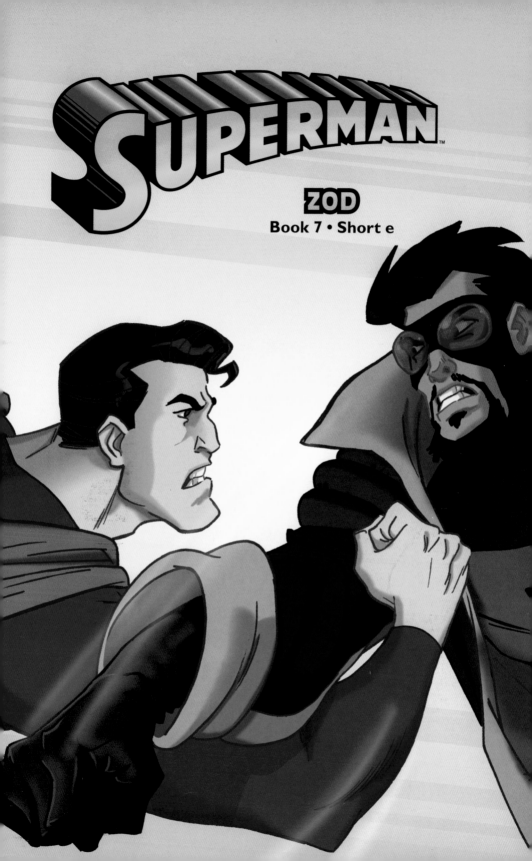

In this story you will learn about the **short e** vowel sound. Can you find these words and sound them out?

end	**enemies**	**fortress**
get	**gets**	**happen**
help	**jets**	**let**
mess	**pets**	**planet**
send	**stretches**	**tells**
them	**threaten**	**yells**

Here are some sight words:

friends	**humans**	**there**

Here are some fun Superman words:

battle	**machine**	**Zod**

General Zod and his evil friends are enemies from Superman's planet.

"We will rule Earth and make humans our pets," they threaten.

Superman cannot let that happen!

"We must send them back to space," Superman tells his friends.

"I know how. But I need your help!"

Superman jets to his fortress.

He has a machine there that

can end this battle.

The others are close behind.

"Get them!" yells Superman.

Wonder Woman stretches her lasso.

Batman gets the machine.

The enemies are trapped!
"That's the end of this mess,"
Superman says.

SUPERMAN™

BIZARRO
Book 8 • Short i

In this story you will learn about the **short i** vowel sound. Can you find these words and sound them out?

big	bits	bridge
city	fix	his
hits	in	is
it	kitten	lifts
rips	river	sinking
things	thinking	will

Here are some sight words:

causes   trouble

Here are some fun Superman words:

alien   Bizarro   heart

Bizarro likes to fix things,

but he only causes trouble.

His thinking is all backward.

Bizarro spies a kitten in a tree.

"Bizarro must save tree!" he says.

He rips it out of the ground.

A boat is sinking in the river. "Bizarro will stop the river," says the alien.

Bizarro hits a bridge hard.

Bits of rock fly down.

The river starts to flood!

Superman has to save the city!
He lifts the boat and the rocks
out of the river.

"You have a big heart," Superman
tells Bizarro.

"But you are a better hero on Bizarro
World!"

SUPERMAN™

SUPER HERO FRIENDS

Book 9 • Short o

In this story you will learn about the **short o** vowel sound. Can you find these words and sound them out?

block	drop	hops
hottest	job	off
problem	shots	solve
spot	stop	toss

Here are some sight words:

against	everything	friends
sometimes	together	trouble
wherever		

Here are some fun Superman words:

Batmobile	bracelets	zooms

It's Superman's job to stop

the bad guys.

But sometimes, he needs

a little help.

Batman and Wonder Woman have skills that help Superman when he's in trouble.

Batman's tools help spot danger.
He hops into the Batmobile
and zooms off wherever he is
needed.

Wonder Woman has bracelets that block against even the hottest laser shots.

If one of them is in trouble,

the friends will drop everything

to toss the bad guys out of town.

When these friends work together,

there is no problem they can't solve.

SUPERMAN

PARASITE

Book 10 • Short u

In this story you will learn about the **short u** vowel sound. Can you find these words and sound them out?

bug	but	hugs
hunts	just	punches
run	runs	stunned
suck	thug	touch
trouble	ultimate	up
upset		

Here are some sight words:

away   laughs   right   tight

Here are some fun Superman words:

energy   hideout   Parasite

Parasite can suck a

person's energy

with just one touch.

He is lots of trouble.

It is up to Superman
to stop this thug!
He hunts down Parasite's
hideout.

"You can't run," Superman shouts.

But Parasite has a plan.

He runs up to Superman

and hugs him tight.

"Now I have ultimate power!"

he cries.

But Superman gets back
up right away.
He punches Parasite.
Parasite is stunned!

"It takes more than one
little bug to upset me."
Superman laughs.

SUPERMAN STARRO

Book 11
Using the sounds of -ch, -sh, and -tch

In this story you will learn about the **-ch**, **-sh**, and **-tch** sounds. Can you find these words and sound them out?

attached	brainwash	catch
changed	charge	chases
check	choppers	dashes
fishy	much	rush
shooting	shout	shrinks
snatches	Washington	

Here are some sight words:

anyone	president
something	voice

Here are some fun Superman words:

probe	Starro	White House

Wonder Woman is at

the White House with Superman.

"There's something fishy

here," she thinks.

"The president's voice

has changed."

Batman rushes to Washington.
They check on the president
and see something attached
to his neck!

"A Starro probe!" they shout.

"Starro can brainwash anyone.

We must catch him!"

Superman takes charge.

He dashes between choppers

that are shooting lasers at him.

Superman chases Starro down.

Wonder Woman snatches him

in her lasso.

Batman shrinks him down.

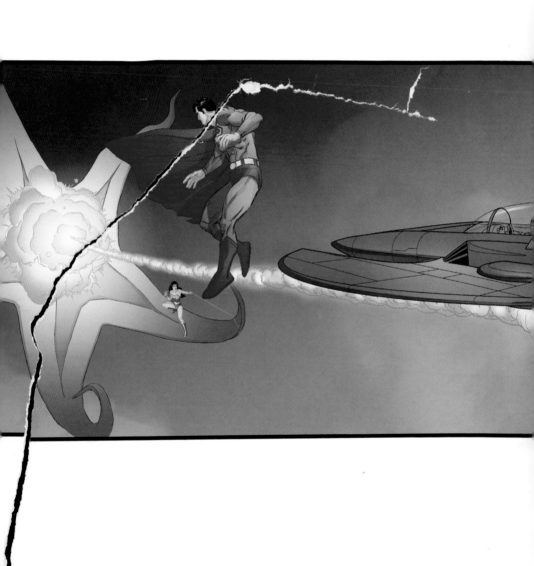

The president is free!

"Thank you so much," he says.

**LEX
LUTHOR**

**Book 12
Review: Long Vowels**

In this story you will review the **long vowel** sounds. Can you find these words and sound them out?

away	beams	blow
evil	eyes	flies
foe	go	hole
laser	mine	police
rages	safely	save
see	stone	time

Here are some sight words:

| building | laughs | toward |

Superman hears an evil threat from his foe Lex Luthor.

"Metropolis is mine," rages Luthor.

"You can't save it!"

"We'll see about that," says Superman.

Superman flies to the city
in time to see Luthor blow
a hole in a building.

A stone crashes toward Lois!

Superman tosses it safely away.

Superman shoots two beams
from his eyes.

They blow up Luthor's laser!

"Time to go to the police!"

Superman laughs.

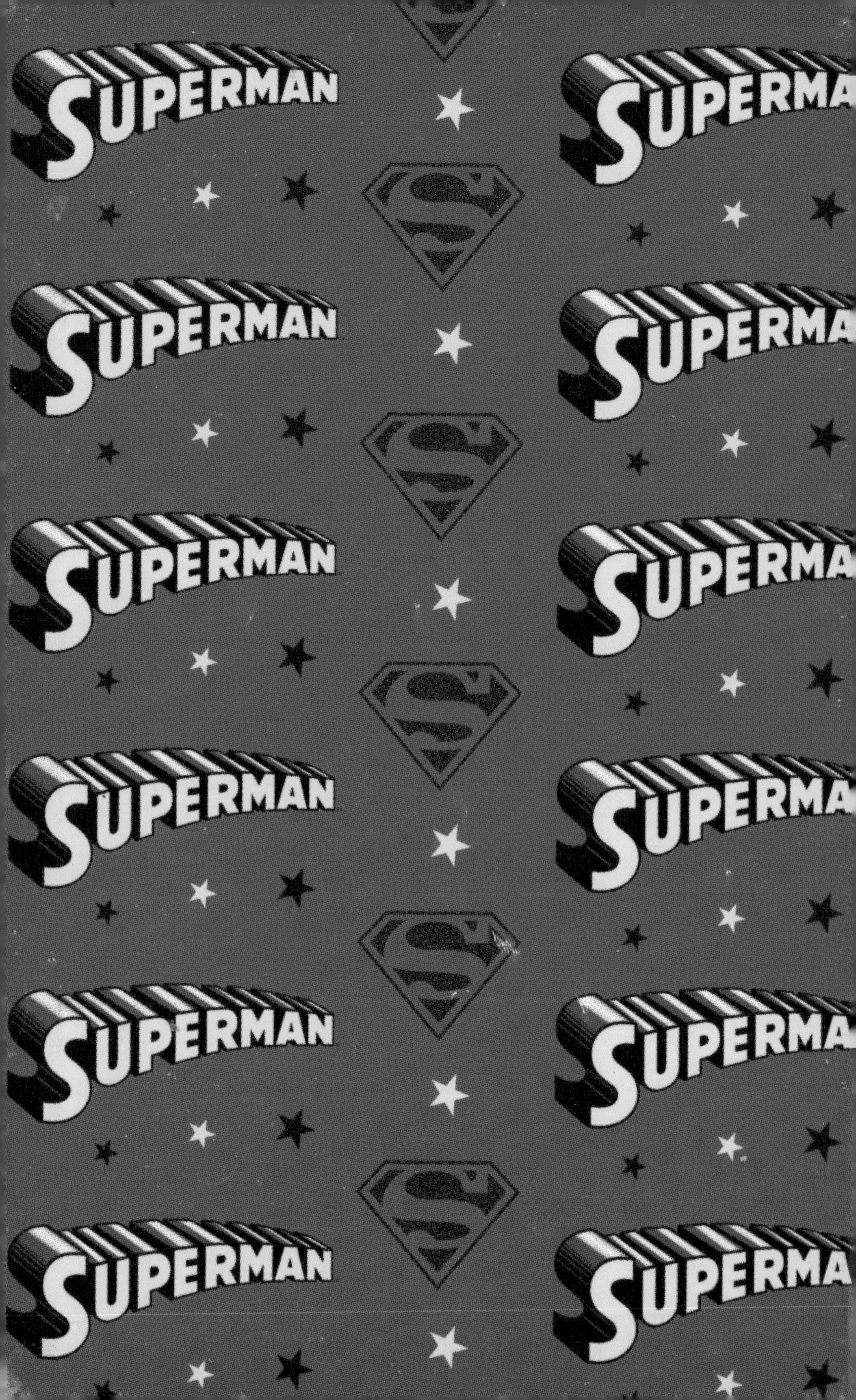
SUPERMAN